THE MOON THAT SHONE DARK

Malcolm the weaver spins his yarns and weaves his magic
to teach children about nature and its colours, about the
environment and about all the things that matter in a young
child's life... So you can understand and treasure the whole
caboodle of being a wee human being.

'The Moon that shone dark' looks at the peril of atmosphere
contamination and foggy pollution. For the world to be a
happy place, the air around us must be clear and fresh.

Written by Malcolm Campbell   Illustrated by Sharon Campbell

Malcolm the weaver wove wonderful dreams on his **magic loom.**

shuttle
treadle
weave pick

Dreams can create and shape whatever your imagination wants them to, in your mind's eye.

The shining Moon dream was a very **strange** and **unusual** dream...
During the day, the sun was tired and weary as it was hard to shine
light and heat through a haze of cloud and pollution.
At night time, the moon rose fresh and full, to shine in the darkness
that the sun had left behind...

The Sun had gone down behind the **horizon** one evening and the **full Moon** shone across the earth. It was dark, it was cold... it was **night time**.

Bats, moles, slugs and worms all came out to feed and to play in the dark. The sun stayed asleep, **exhausted** after shining through the fog that covered the earth.

The birds slept with their heads under their wings. Children slept with their heads under their covers. Animals slept under trees and hedges. It was time for the **night creatures** to come out!

Next morning, when it should have been light, there was **no light**. Oh no! It **stayed dark**. The Sun did not wake up, the Moon could not go to bed. Every single thing had changed. The whole shebang was different. Bats started singing like banshees **'creeeoak, creeeoak'**, it was not a nice sound.

Moles came out and danced on the grass. It was not strictly dancing, their feet were too big and they tripped and fell.

Birds could not fly, it was dark and they could not see where they were going. Children slept and slept and slept. **Oh no no no**!

SHUTTLE TREADLE
WEAVE PICK
SHUTTLE
TREADLE WEAVE
PICK ON AND ON
HE WOVE
SHUTTLE
TREADLE
WEAVE
PICK

Malcolm the weaver went to his **magic handloom** and wove a **magic spell** to make the dawn chorus chirrup again. On and on he wove until little clear patches could be seen in the sky.

Malcolm knew that all around the world, if factories and cars did not stop pumping **smoke** and **exhaust fumes** into the atmosphere, one day it may become dark and cold forever and ever, with no **sunlight** to be seen ever again.

Slowly, the Sun began to rise slightly, then it slipped back down again. The world became a little light, then went dark again....

The weaver wove on. **Shuttle, treadle, weave, pick.** On and on. Shuttle, treadle, weave, pick.

Slowly the loom wove on, until there was light, a little light at first, then more. Eventually the air cleared and the sunshine could spread across the earth again.

The Sun rose higher and higher...'Good Morning!'.
The Moon yawned and went to bed. The worms and moles quickly
went back to the dark underground. The bats quickly flew back in to
their dark caves and the birds sang their favourite songs because
they had songs to sing.

The magic spell was woven. Bumblebees flew around the trees and the flowers bloomed again. The sun shone brightly and Roddy and Mairi laughed and played again. Clear light and warmth loomed over the whole caboodle. The world was a bright and happy place to be!

THE MOON THAT SHONE DARK

THE
END

Goodnight

Z Z
Z

THE RAINBOW THAT MIXED COLOURS

TH
END

now turn the book upside down to start the next story...

THE MOON THAT SHONE DARK

The magic spell was woven. The rainbow colours shone and sparkled in the sun. Colour, love and peace loomed over the whole caboodle. The world was a colourful and fun place to be!

The weaver wove on. **Shuttle, treadle, weave, pick.** On and on. Shuttle, treadle, weave, pick, until the loom wove the colours into the correct order, from red to orange, yellow to green then blue to indigo and violet.

Shuttle
treadle
weave
pick
Shuttle
treadle
weave
pick

Slowly the loom wove on, until the sky turned blue and trees rustled green. Roddy and Mairi looked like themselves again. Mother nature looked upon the face of the cloth on Malcolm's magic loom and knew that this was it. This was how the true colours in nature's spectrum should be.

The sea became **purple** like blackcurrant juice, the sky turned **green** like peas. Trees were as **yellow** as a submarine and people were bright **blue**!

But that wasn't right! These colours were not true and correct. **Oh no no no!**

The rainbow colours started to alter and change. Slowly they moved back to nearly the correct order as the **sun shone** on the crystal clear water.

Malcolm knew that all around the world, if **waste** and **rubbish** is pumped into the sea and nasty **smelly pollution** clogs the rivers, sea and atmosphere, the colours of the rainbow may turn grey forever and ever.

SHUTTLE TREADLE WEAVE PICK!
SHUTTLE TREADLE WEAVE PICK! ON AND ON HE WOVE
SHUTTLE TREADLE WEAVE PICK!

Malcolm the weaver went to his **magic handloom** and wove a **magic spell** to bring the colours and shades back together again, as nature intended. Red became orange then yellow then green then blue then indigo and violet.

There was a primary mix up of all the colour combinations within the rainbow. **Oh no!**

Red and **yellow** no longer made **orange**, they now made **green**! **Yellow** and **blue** no longer made **green**, they now made **purple** and **purple** was no longer created from **blue** and **red**, they now made **orange**!

The rainbow was **confused** and **muddled**. It was puzzled as all the colours had changed and were mixed up. The whole shebang was different.

The colours of the rainbow had become all mixed up as the sun shone off the dirty water. **Everything had changed hue.** Red was followed by green instead of orange and blue was followed by yellow instead of indigo and violet. Oh no!

The sea was red like jelly, the sky was yellow like custard. Trees were purple and all the earth's people were as green as grass.

The rainbow dream was a very **odd** and **unusual** dream...
Pollution of the rivers and sea had changed the way that the sun
shone colours on the world...

Malcolm the weaver wove wonderful **dreams** on his magic loom.

shuttle
treadle
weave
pick

Dreams can create and shape whatever your imagination wants them to, in your mind's eye.

THE RAINBOW THAT MIXED COLOURS

Malcolm the Weaver

Malcolm the weaver spins his yarns and weaves his magic to teach children about nature and its colours, about the environment and about all the things that matter in a young child's life... So you can understand and treasure the whole caboodle of being a wee human being.

'The Rainbow that mixed colours' looks at the dangers of global pollution in the rivers and sea. For the world to be a happy place, the waters must become crystal clear once more.

Written by Malcolm Campbell   Illustrated by Sharon Campbell

This book is dedicated to my children **Gary**, **Roslyn**, **Dawn**, **Sharon**, **Catriona**, **Aidan** and **Zoe**, who are the wellspring of my humility and the dignity and the flowing souce of my happiness.
Malcolm Campbell

society of dyers and colourists

Educating the changing world in the science of colour

Published by the Society of Dyers and Colourists
PO Box 244, Perkin House, 82 Grattan Road,
Bradford, West Yorkshire, BD1 2JB, England
www.sdc.org.uk www.colour.sdc.org.uk

ISBN 978-0-901956-95-8

Printed by Think Digital Books / Weston-super-Mare, Somerset